The Adventures of
Pia the Peruvian Cat

By Renee Burney
Illustrated By Bethany McElroy

Creative Life Publishing & Learning Institute
www.CLPLI.com
Info@CLPLI.com

Book Versions
Ingram ISBN: 978-1-946265-33-3
KDP Paperback ISBN: 978-1-946265-34-0
eBook ISBN: 978-1-946265-35-7

Illustrated By Bethany McElroy
Book Layout Design By Dara Rogers

The Adventures of Pia the Peruvian Cat

It is hot in Peru. One day a nice lady I have never seen before noticed me laying in the shade under a car outside the hotel.

She knelt down and called me, "here kitty kitty" and I came running up to her. I rubbed up against her legs and greeted her with a soft "meow."

"Aren't you a sweet little cat" she said. Then she scratched my head and got on a bus.

You see, I am a street cat. I have no home. I have nobody to love me. Nobody to feed me and nowhere to sleep at night.

9

Later that afternoon I heard that same familiar sound, "here kitty kitty." I popped up from my nap and looked around. There she was. That nice lady again. She scratched my head and went back in the hotel.

I thought to myself, "I really like that lady."

The next morning, I was waiting on the sidewalk outside the hotel. "Where is she" I thought?

Then I found her. She had something with her that smelled SOOOOO good! Was it for me? I was so hungry.

"Here kitty kitty."

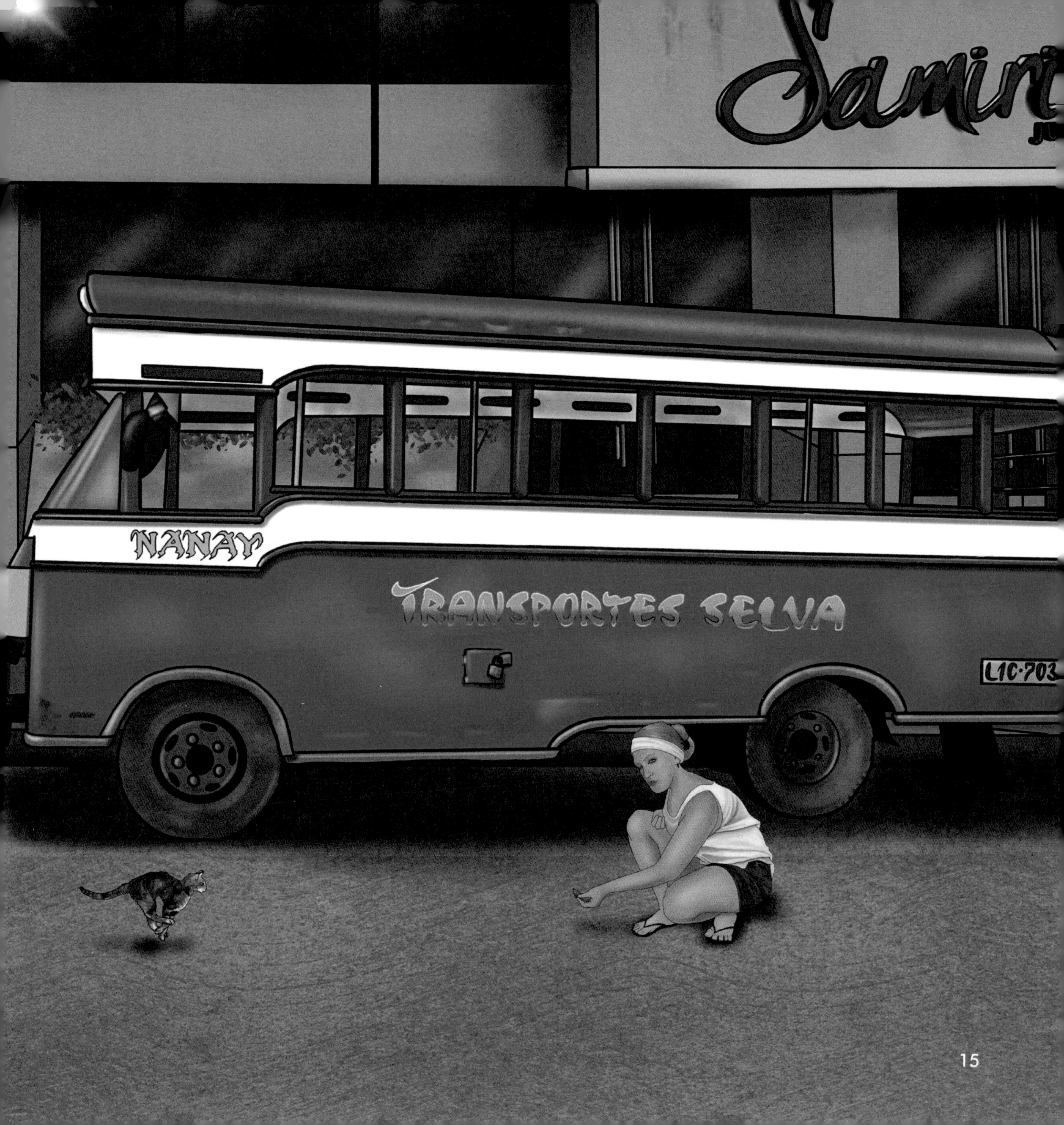
NANAY
TRANSPORTES SELVA
L1C·703

She pulled out a handful of Jerky and made them into little pieces just for me.

I heard the man she was with say, "are you feeding this street cat part of our lunch?"

"She is starving honey, we will be ok."

Then she scratched my head and jumped back on the bus.

Later that afternoon when she got back to the hotel, I must have missed her because I didn't see her.

After dinner with her friends she came outside and met me on the sidewalk. She brought left over chicken from dinner but I was not feeling good. I was coughing and tired. I just wanted to lay down.

The nice lady picked me up and put me in her arms. We jumped in the back of a motorcar and rushed to the vet.

Turns out, I had a fever and was very sick. The doctor wanted me to stay the night.

23

Everyday the lady came to visit me. She even brought her husband. I liked him too. He had a big beard that I liked to rub against.

I heard the lady say that they were leaving in a few days to go back to America. She told the doctor that she wanted to take me home, but the doctor said I was too sick to travel right now.

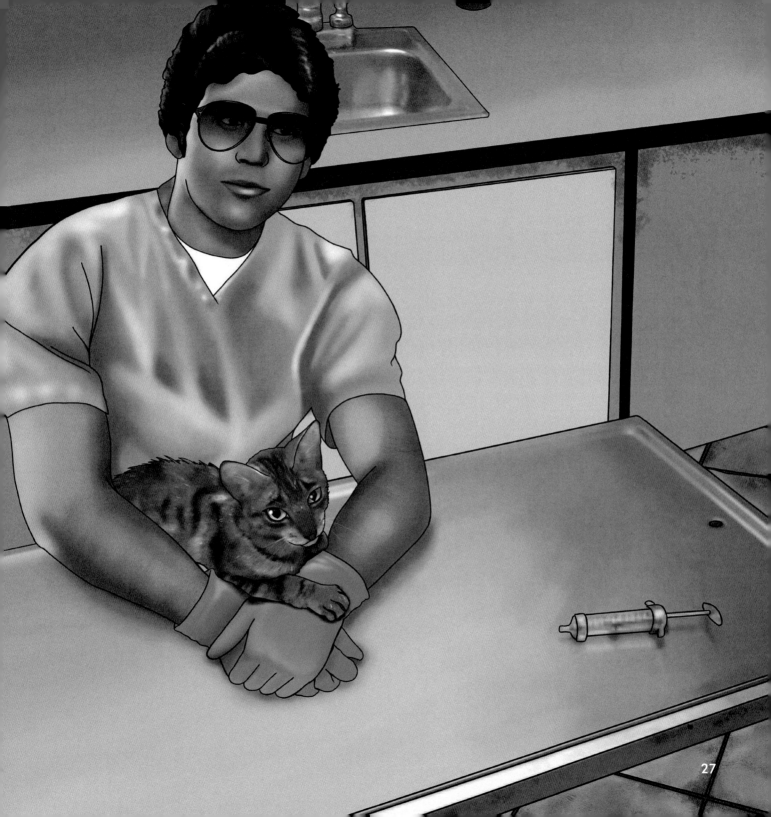

I really liked my new friends and wanted to go to America to be with them. I would try hard to get well and put on weight so I would be strong enough for a trip.

I ate a lot, napped a lot and the medicine started to make me feel better. I was going to be ok.

Could I still go to America? What about my new friends? Would I ever see them again?

Then one day a different lady came to pick me up. I had no idea where I was going. Next thing I knew I was getting on an airplane.

When I got off the airplane, I was in Los Angeles.

Then I heard the sweetest voice say, "here kitty kitty."

Was it really her?

Yes, it was!

We were together at last. I finally have someone to love me.

Made in the USA
Coppell, TX
28 January 2021